Choral and Perf... Poetry

Selected by Fiona Waters

For Marjolijn, with love.

Contents

Longman

Edinburgh Gate
Harlow, Essex

Sea Timeless Song

Hurricane come
and hurricane go
but sea – sea timeless
sea timeless
sea timeless
sea timeless

Hibiscus bloom
then dry wither so
but sea – sea timeless
sea timeless
sea timeless
sea timeless

Tourist come
and tourist go
but sea – sea timeless
sea timeless
sea timeless
sea timeless

Grace Nichols

Micky Always

Bambalitty-Bambam,
Bambalitty-Bambam,
Everybody scram, scram.

Micky hit the ball so hard
it gone right out the yard
and break the lady window-pane
He Micky don't hear, just don't hear.

Bambalitty-Bambam,
Bambalitty-Bambam,
Everybody scram, scram.

Micky break the lady window-pane
and when the lady come and complain
Mammy going give he plai-plai
then you going to hear Micky cry.

John Agard

Lotus Flower Takeaway

Number one
Egg Foo Yung
Number two
Chicken with Bamboo
Number three
Shrimp Chop Suey
Number four
Rice galore
Number five
Forget your knife
Number six
Chopsticks
Number seven
Mmm, this is heaven
Number eight
Forget your weight
Number nine
Hands off, that's mine
Number ten
Same again!

Jennifer and Graeme Curry

I Will Give You the Keys of Heaven

I will give you the keys of heaven,
I will give you the keys of heaven,
Madam, will you walk? Madam, will you talk?
Madam, will you walk and talk with me?

Though you give me the keys of heaven,
Though you give me the keys of heaven,
Yet I will not walk; no, I will not talk;
No, I will not walk or talk with thee.

I will give you a blue silk gown,
To make you fine when you go to town;
Madam, will you walk? Madam, will you talk?
Madam, will you walk and talk with me?

Though you give me a blue silk gown,
To make me fine when I go to town;
Yet I will not walk; no, I will not talk;
No, I will not walk or talk with thee.

I will give you a coach and six,
Six black horses as black as pitch;
Madam, will you walk? Madam, will you talk?
Madam, will you walk and talk with me?

Though you give me a coach and six,
Six black horses as black as pitch;
Yet I will not walk; no, I will not talk;
No, I will not walk or talk with thee.

I will give you the keys of my heart,
And we'll be married till death us do part;
Madam, will you walk? Madam, will you talk?
Madam, will you walk and talk with me?

Thou shalt give me the keys of thy heart,
And we'll be married till death us do part;
I will walk, I will talk,
I will walk and talk with thee.

Traditional

The Mermaid

One Friday morn when we set sail,
And our ship not far from land,
We there did spy a pretty, pretty maid,
With a comb and a glass in her hand, her hand, her hand,
With a comb and a glass in her hand.

> While the raging seas did roar,
> And the stormy winds did blow,
> And we jolly sailor boys were up a-loft,
> And the land-lubbers lying down below, below, below,
> And the land-lubbers lying down below.

And then up spoke the captain of our ship,
Who at once our peril did seem,
"I have married a wife in fair London town,
And tonight she a widow will be, will be, will be,
And tonight she a widow will be."

> While the raging seas did roar,
> And the stormy winds did blow,
> And we jolly sailor boys were up a-loft,
> And the land-lubbers lying down below, below, below,
> And the land-lubbers lying down below.

And then up spoke the little cabin boy,
And a fair-haired boy was he,
"I've a father and a mother in fair Portsmouth town,
And tonight they will weep for me, for me, for me,
And tonight they will weep for me."

While the raging seas did roar,
And the stormy winds did blow,
And we jolly sailor boys were up a-loft,
And the land-lubbers lying down below, below, below,
And the land-lubbers lying down below.

The three times round went our gallant ship,
And three times round went she,
Then three times round when our gallant, gallant ship,
And she sank to the bottom of the sea, the sea, the sea,
And she sank to the bottom of the sea

While the raging seas did roar,
And the stormy winds did blow,
And we jolly sailor boys were up a-loft,
And the land-lubbers lying down below, below, below,
And the land-lubbers lying down below.

Traditional

What Turkey Doing?

Mosquito one
mosquito two
mosquito jump
in de old man shoe

Cockroach three
cockroach four
cockroach dance thru
a crack in de floor

Spider five
spider six
spider weaving
a web of tricks

Monkey seven
monkey eight
monkey playing with
pencil and slate

Turkey nine
turkey ten
what turkey doing
in chicken pen?

John Agard

Bears Don't Like Bananas

Monkeys like to play the drums,
    badgers wear bandannas.
Tigers like to tickle toes
    but bears don't like bananas.

A crocodile can juggle buns
    on visits to his Nana's
Seagulls like to dance and sing
    but bears don't like bananas.

Rats and mice can somersault
    and do gymnastics with iguanas.
Weasels like to wiggle their legs
    but bears don't like bananas.

A porcupine likes drinking tea,
    and cheering at gymkhanas.
A ladybird likes eating pies
    but bears don't like bananas.

John Rice

The Wraggle Taggle Gipsies

Three gipsies stood at the castle gate,
And they sang so high, they sang so low,
The lady sate in her chamber late,
Her heart it melted away as snow.

They sang so sweet, they sang so shrill,
That fast her tears began to flow,
And she laid down her silken gown,
Her golden rings and all her show.

She plucked off her high-heeled shoes,
A-made of Spanish leather, O.
She would in the street, with her bare, bare feet,
All out in the wind and weather, O.

"O saddle to me my milk-white steed,
And go and fetch me my pony, O.
That I may ride and seek my bride,
Who is gone with the wraggle taggle gipsies, O."

O he rode high, and he rode low,
He rode through wood and copses too,
Until he came to an open field,
And there he espied his a-lady, O.

"What makes you leave your house and land,
Your golden treasures for to go?
What makes you leave your new-wedded
lord,
To follow the wraggle taggle gipsies, O?"

"What care I for my house and land?
What care I for my treasure, O?
What care I for my new-wedded lord?
I'm off with the wraggle, taggle gipsies, O!"

"Last night you slept on a goose-feather bed,
With the sheet turned down so bravely, O.
Tonight you'll sleep in a cold open field,
Along with the wraggle taggle gipsies, O."

"What care I for a goose-feather bed,
With the sheet turned down so bravely, O?
Tonight I'll sleep in a cold open field,
Along with the wraggle taggle gipsies, O."

Traditional

Up On the Downs

Up on the Downs,
Up on the Downs,
A skylark flutters
And the fox barks shrill,
Brown rabbit scutters
And the hawk hangs still.
Up on the Downs,
Up on the Downs,
With butterflies
        jigging
                like
                        costumed
                                clowns.

Here in the Hills,
Here in the Hills,
The long grass flashes
And the sky seems vast,
Rock lizard dashes
And a crow flies past.
Here in the Hills,
Here in the Hills,
With bumble bees
        buzzing
                like
                        high-speed
                                drills.

High on the Heath,
High on the Heath,
The slow-worm slithers
And the trees are few,
Field-mouse dithers
And the speedwell's blue.
High on the Heath,
High on the Heath,
Where grasshoppers
   chirp
      in the
         grass
            beneath.

Wes Magee

All of Us Knocking on the Stable Door

Three great kings, three wise men,
Tramp across the desert to Bethlehem
Arrive at the inn, don't travel no more
They start knocking at the stable door.

Knocking at the door, knocking at the door
All of us are knocking at the stable door.

I've got myrrh, he's got gold
He's got frankincense and all of us are cold
We stand here shivering, chilled to the core
We're just knocking on the stable door.

The star above it glows in the sky
Burning up the darkness and we know why
A baby King's asleep in the straw
So we start knocking on the stable door.

Travelled some distance, we've travelled far
Melchior, Casper and Balthazaar
We're so wealthy, the baby's so poor
But here we are knocking on the stable door.

Now is the time, now is the hour
To feel the glory, worship the power
We quietly enter, kneel on the floor
Just the other side of the stable door.

Knocking on the door, knocking on the door
All of us knocking at the stable door.

Knocking on the door, knocking on the door
All of us knocking at the stable door.

David Harmer

17

Rhythm

Rhythm rhythm
Can you
Hear the
Rhythm

If you listen close
Ears to the ground
The base of noise
Is rhythm's sound
From spoken words
To ways of walk
from rapping to reggae
And funk we talk in

Rhythm rhythm
Can you
Hear the
Rhythm

Way back in the heart of Africa
They took our drums away
But rhythm proved its own power
By being here today

All four corners
Sweet sounding Rhythms reach
With treble in the speakers
And bass in the speech
From the depths of cold
To heat in heights
Mohammid Ali did do it in fights

With
Quick Rhythms
Slick Rhythms
Bold Rhythms
Gold Rhythms
God given
Rhythm Rhythm
Can you
hear the
Rhythm Rhythm

Rhythm rhythm
Can you
hear the
Rhythm

Lemn Sissay

Left or Right?

When we all went for a picnic
Mum drove the car
And Dad was navigator.

"Are you sure
you can read the map?"
Mum asked.
"Of course I can."
Dad said.

We got out into the country
"Right."
Said Dad.
"At the next junction
turn left. Right?"
So Mum turned right.

"Look, I said left."
"You said right."
"Well, get us back then."
"OK."

Dad folded the map.
"Now,"
he said
"Turn left, then right. Right?"
"Turn right."
"No. Left."

"Left?"
"That's right."
"But you said left, not right."
"Right. Left."
Mum stopped the car.

Her face was traffic light red.
"We're going home."
She said.
"But Mum …"
we all said.
She narrowed her eyes.
"Look, I'm quite happy
to leave you all here.
So be quiet or you'll be
Left. Right?"
"Right."
We said.

We had our picnic
In the garden.
Dad said
"We could try again
tomorrow."
Mum raised her fists.
"Which do you want?"
she said
"Left or right?"

Robin Mellor

21

Smuggler's Song

If you wake at midnight, and hear a horse's feet,
Don't go drawing back the blind, or looking in the street,
Them that ask no questions isn't told a lie.
Watch the wall, my darling, while the Gentlemen go by!
    Five and twenty ponies,
    Trotting through the dark –
    Brandy for the Parson,
    'Baccy for the Clerk.
    Laces for a lady, letters for a spy,
And watch the wall, my darling, while the Gentlemen go by!

Running round the woodlump if you chance to find
Little barrels, roped and tarred, all full of brandy-wine,
Don't you shout to come and look, nor use 'em for your play.
Put the brushwood back again – and they'll be gone next day!

If you see the stable-door setting open wide;
If you see a tired horse lying down inside;
If your mother mends a coat cut about and tore;
If the lining's wet and warm – don't you ask no more!

If you meet King George's men, dressed in blue and red,
You be careful what you say, and mindful what is said.
If they call you 'pretty maid', and chuck you 'neath the chin,
Don't you tell where no one is, nor yet where no one's been!

Knocks and footsteps round the house – whistles after dark –
You've no call for running out till the house-dogs bark.
Trusty's here, and *Pincher's* here, and see how dumb they lie –
They don't fret to follow when the Gentlemen go by!

If you do as you've been told, 'likely there's a chance,
You'll be give a dainty doll, all the way from France,
With a cap of Valenciennes, and a velvet hood –
A present from the Gentlemen, along o' being good!
    Five and twenty ponies,
    Trotting through the dark –
    Brandy for the Parson,
    'Baccy for the Clerk.
Them that ask no questions isn't told a lie –
And watch the wall, my darling, while the Gentlemen go by!

Rudyard Kipling

Patchwork Rap

I'm a touch lazy
Don't like doing much work
But often get the itch
To pitch into some patchwork
It may be a hotchpotch
Like fretwork or such work
When I slough on my couch
And fetch out my patchwork

First I snatch a patch
From the batch in my pouch
But the patch doesn't match
The patches on my patchwork
So I catch another patch
From the batch in my satchel
And this one matches
The patches on my patchwork
So I take my patch
Attach it with stitches
Patch against patch
Where the patchwork matches
But if it doesn't match
Even after it's attached
Then the mismatched stitch
Has to be detached …

You know
I don't like thatchwork
Don't like ditchwork
Only kind I favour
Is my patchwork stitchwork
And soon my patchwork's
Going like clockwork
Sharper than a pitchfork
Neater than brickwork

24

Hotter than a firework
Cooler than a waxwork

So I snatch a patch
From the batch in my pouch
But the patch doesn't match
The patches on my patchwork
So I catch another patch
From the batch in my satchel
And this one matches
The patches on my patchwork
So I take my patch
Attach it with stitches
Patch against patch
Where the patchwork matches
And I keep on patching
Till everything's matching
And I keep on stitching
Till I've filled up the kitchen
With my rich rich rich rich
Wider than a soccer pitch
Wonderful colourful magical patchwork quilt!

Now which stitch is which?

Adrian Mitchell

Conversation Piece

Late again Blenkinsop?
What's the excuse this time?
Not my fault sir.
Whose fault is it then?
Grandma's sir.
Grandma's. What did she do?
She died sir.
Died?
She's seriously dead all right sir.
That makes four grandmothers this term.
And all on P.E. days Blenkinsop.
I know. It's very upsetting sir.
How many grandmothers have you got Blenkinsop?
Grandmothers sir? None sir.
None?
All dead sir.
And what about yesterday Blenkinsop?
What about yesterday sir?
You missed maths.
That was the dentist sir.
The dentist died?
No sir. My teeth sir.
You missed the test Blenkinsop.
I'd been looking forward to it too sir.
Right, line up for P.E.
Can't sir.
No such word as can't. Why can't you?

No kit sir.
Where is it?
Home sir.
What's it doing at
home?
Not ironed sir.
Couldn't you iron it?
Can't do it sir.
Why not?
My hand sir.
Who usually does it?
Grandma sir.
Why couldn't she do it?
Dead sir.

Gareth Owen

Daughter of the Sea

bog seeper
moss creeper
growing restless getting steeper

trickle husher
swish and rusher
stone leaper splash and gusher

foam flicker
mirror slicker
pebble pusher boulder kicker

still pool
don't be fooled
shadow tricker keeping cool

leap lunger
crash plunger
free fall with thunder under

garbage binner
dump it in her
never mind her dog's dinner

plastic bagger
old lagger
oil skinner wharf nagger

cargo porter
weary water
tide dragger long lost daughter

of the sea
the sea the sea
has caught her up in its arms and set her free

Philip Gross

Night Mail

I

This is the Night Mail crossing the Border,
Bringing the cheque and the postal order,
Letters for the rich, letters for the poor,
The shop at the corner, the girl next door.
Pulling up Beattock, a steady climb:
The gradient's against her, but she's on time.

Past cotton-grass and moorland boulder,
Shovelling white steam over her shoulder,
Snorting noisily, she passes
Silent miles of wind-bent grasses.

Birds turn their heads as she approaches,
Stare from the bushes at her blank-faced coaches.
Sheep-dogs cannot turn her course;
They slumber on with paws across.
In the farm she passes no one wakes,
But a jug in a bedroom gently shakes.

II

Dawn freshens. Her climb is done.
Down towards Glasgow she descends
Towards the stream tugs yelping down a glade of cranes
Towards the fields of apparatus, the furnaces
Set on the dark plain like gigantic chessmen.
All Scotland waits for her:
In dark glens, beside pale-green lochs,
Men long for news.

III

Letters of thanks, letters from banks,
Letters of joy from girl and boy,
Receipted bills and invitations
to inspect new stock or to visit relations,
And applications for situations,
And timid lovers' declarations,
And gossip, gossip from all the nations,
　　News circumstantial, news financial,
　　Letters with holiday snaps to enlarge in,
　　Letters with faces scrawled on the margin,
　　Letters from uncles, cousins and aunts,
　　Letters to Scotland from the South of France,
　　Letters of condolence to Highlands and Lowlands
　　Notes from overseas to Hebrides –
　　Written on paper of every hue,
　　The pink, the violet, the white and the blue,
The chatty, the catty, the boring, the adoring,
The cold and official and the heart's outpouring,
Clever, stupid, short and long,
The typed and the printed and the spelt all wrong.

IV

Thousands are still asleep,
Dreaming of terrifying monsters
Or a friendly tea beside the band in Cranston's or Crawford's.
Asleep in working Glasgow, asleep in well-set Edinburgh,
Asleep in granite Aberdeen.
They continue their dreams,
But shall wake soon and hope for letters,
And none will hear the postman's knock
Without a quickening of the heart.
For who can bear to feel himself forgotten?

W. H. Auden

32